# ALL MY COLORS

Written By L. T. James

Illustrated By Kelsey Marshalsey

Written by L.T. James
Illustrated by Kelsey Marshalsey

Copyright © 2022 by L.T. James

Paperback ISBN: 978-1-958763-07-0
Hardcover ISBN: 978-1-958763-06-3
ebook ISBN: 978-1-958763-08-7

To my first born, who has always
been unapologetically himself.
I love all your colors,
no matter what they are.

He walked down the hall just singing a tune.
With his bright, rainbow colors, and his bright, happy mood.

But not one child smiled, and not one matched with him.
They just stopped, and they stared, because he wasn't like them.

They whispered, and they pointed. "Which color here are you?"
"It's an easy choice you see, are you pink or are you blue?"

He frowned, and he thought, and then he looked all around.
"I don't want to be just one, I like all that I've found."

"You can only be one, that's what everyone says.
It's blue or it's pink, that's just the way that it is."

"Pinks dote on others with love and with care.

They push babies in strollers and wear bows in their hair."

"Blues are athletic, with strong arms and no tears.

They must always be fierce and show zero fears."

"You can only be one, that's what everyone says.
It's blue or it's pink, that's just the way that it is."

"Well, hm," he said, frowning. "That certainly is strange.
But it doesn't have to be true and doesn't mean it can't change."

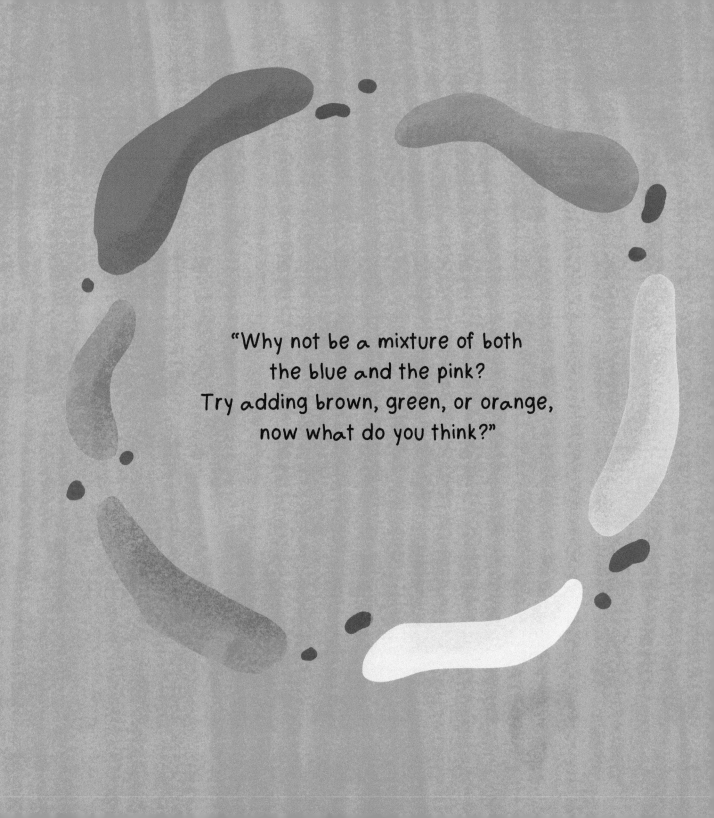

"Why not be a mixture of both
the blue and the pink?
Try adding brown, green, or orange,
now what do you think?"

"I am many different colors, and I think I look fine.
It's okay to change old rules that claim rainbows can't shine."

The friends glanced at each other, and their frowns turned to glee.
"Will you show us your colors? Oh, will you? Pretty please?"

"Sit down, sit down, I will show you one by one.
For each has its own meaning, and each one is equal fun."

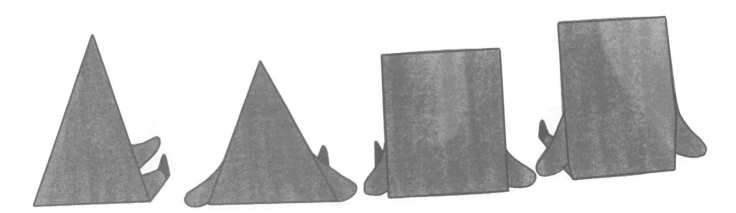

"I am loving and caring
and fearless and strong,
But there are so many others,
and not one of them is wrong."

"Red makes me happy and reminds me of life.
I value each member, and I try not to fight."

"Orange wraps me up until I'm happy and snug,
And it taught me all healing can start with a hug."

"Yellow like a lightbulb, I have ideas I want to try.
Just like you, and you, and you, we can be great if we apply."

"Green stands for growth, so when I'm feeling super down,
I remember even the tallest trees started from the ground."

"Blue can, indeed, be brave and fierce and strong,
But baby blue is calming, and that shade can still belong."

"Pink is often caring and full of grace, it's true,
But pink can also represent the beauty in power too."

"Purple like the spark that blooms inside when I am proud.
My spirit sparkles beautifully when I let my voice be loud."

"Black and brown are important, as is inclusivity.
I believe in a world that practices beautiful diversity."

"These colors make me who I am,
and they'll do the same for you.
Be proud of who you are,
and show the world what you can do."

"When you let your colors show, look how wonderful it can be.
The world is so much brighter when we let our true selves free."

Lightning Source UK Ltd.
Milton Keynes UK
UKHW051811040123
414790UK00003B/19

9 781958 763063